St. Pius X Catholic Primary School
Schneider Road
Barrow-in-Furness
Cumbria, LA14 4AA
Tel: 01229 894651 Fax: 01229 894652

Tips for Reading Together

Children learn best when reading is fun.

- Talk about the title and the pictures on the cover.
- Discuss what you think the story might be about.
- Read the story together, inviting your child to read as much of it as they can.
- Give lots of praise as your child reads, and help them when necessary.
- Try different ways of helping if they get stuck on a word. For example, get them to say the first sound of the word, or break it into chunks, or read the whole sentence again, trying to guess the word. Focus on the meaning.
- Have fun finding the mini monsters in the pictures.
- Re-read the story later, encouraging your child to read as much of it as they can.

Children enjoy re-reading stories and this helps to build their confidence.

Have fun!

Find all the mini monsters in the pictures.

The Hairy-Scary Monster

Written by Cynthia Rider

Illustrated by Alex Brychta

OXFORD

UNIVERSITY PRESS

Kipper didn't want to go to sleep.
"Biff and Chip are at Gran's," he
said. "I don't like being on my own."

"Poor Kipper," thought Floppy.

"I'll stay with him."

"Oh no, Floppy," said Mum.

"Kipper is going to sleep."

But Kipper wasn't going to sleep.
He was wide awake.

"I can't go to sleep," he grumbled.
"I just can't!"

Kipper laughed. "I know! I'll play a trick," he said. "I'll trick Dad and get him to come upstairs."

He jumped up and down on his bed. "Dad!" he yelled. "There's a hairy-scary monster! It's coming to get me, Dad. Help!"

Dad ran up to Kipper's bedroom.
Floppy barked and ran after him.
"What monster?" said Dad.
"Where is it?"

Kipper pointed to the curtains.
"It's behind the curtains," he said.
"It's got sharp yellow teeth and
glowing red eyes."

Dad looked behind the curtains,
but he didn't see a monster.

"There's no monster here," he
said. "Look!"

"It was a trick," laughed Kipper.
"It was just a trick!"

Dad laughed, and tucked Kipper
up. "Be a good boy and go to sleep,"
he said. "And no more tricks!"

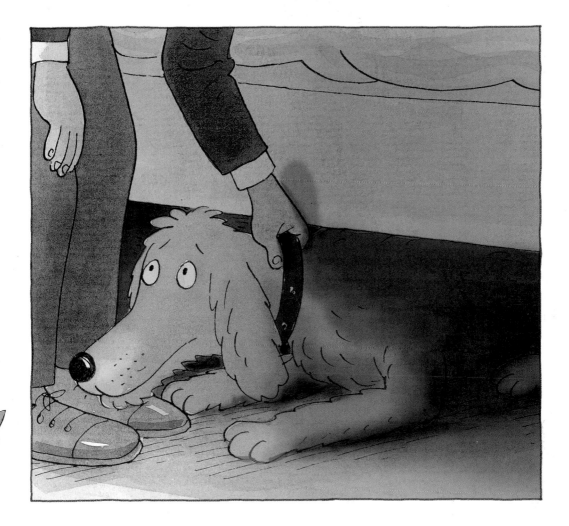

Floppy was hiding. He didn't
like monsters.

"Come out, Floppy," said Dad.
"Kipper is going to sleep."

But Kipper wasn't going to sleep.
He was still wide awake.

"I don't like being on my own,"
he grumbled. "It's boring."

Kipper laughed. "I know! I'll play
another trick," he said. "I'll trick
Mum and get her to come upstairs."

"Mum!" yelled Kipper. "There's a hairy-scary monster! It's going to eat me up. Mum, help!"

Mum ran up to Kipper's bedroom.
Floppy barked and ran after her.

"What monster?" said Mum.

"Where is it?"

Kipper pointed to the wardrobe.
"It's in the wardrobe," he said.
"It's got long sharp claws and
hairy jaws."

Mum looked in the wardrobe, but she didn't see a monster.

"There's no monster here," she said. "Look!"

"It was a trick!" laughed Kipper.
"It was just a trick."

Mum tucked Kipper up again.
"Be a good boy and go to sleep,"
she said. "And no more tricks!"

Kipper began to fall asleep. His
eyes were just closing when he heard
something under the bed.

It was something that was snuffling.
It was something that was snorting. It
was something that was hairy and
very, very scary!

SNUFFLE

SNORT

"Help!" yelled Kipper. "There really is a monster! Mum, Dad, help me! I'm scared!"

Mum and Dad ran upstairs.

"What's wrong, Kipper?" they said.

"There's a monster," he sobbed.

"There's a monster under the bed."

Dad looked under the bed.
"There is a monster!" he said. "It's
the Hairy-Scary Floppy Monster!"

Think about the story

Why didn't Kipper want to go to sleep?

Which three places did Kipper say the monster was hiding?

What things made you laugh in the story?

What makes you scared?

Hide and Seek

What is the monster hiding from? Find the words that rhyme. The words that are left tell you what the monster is hiding from.

claws

trick

hairy

man

mouse

little

pan

stick

jaws

scary

Useful common words repeated in this story and other books in the series. after behind being can't didn't don't help just know laughed more something there's under upstairs

Names in this story: Mum Dad Biff Chip Gran Kipper Floppy

More books for you to enjoy

Level 1: Getting Ready

Level 2: Starting to Read

Level 3: Becoming a Reader

Level 4: Building Confidence

Level 5: Reading with Confidence

OXFORD
UNIVERSITY PRESS

Great Clarendon Street,
Oxford OX2 6DP

Text © Cynthia Rider 2006
Illustrations © Alex Brychta 2006
Designed by Andy Wilson
This edition published 2010

First published 2006
All rights reserved

Series Editors: Kate Ruttle,
Annemarie Young

British Library Cataloguing
in Publication Data available

ISBN: 9780198387732

10 9 8 7 6 5 4 3 2 1

Printed in China by Imago

Have more fun with Read at Home